A CUT ABOVE THE REST

A basic guide to cutting and marker-making for the apparel industry

by
Rose Samuels

and
Ronnie Hoffman

A CUT ABOVE THE REST

A basic guide to marker-making and cutting
for the apparel industry

by
Rose Samuels
and
Ronnie Hoffman

illustrated by
Tony Kentuck

published in Australia
by
PUBLISHING AND PRODUCTION PROJECTS PTY LTD
P O Box 1000   Potts Point   NSW 2011

manuscript developed in association with
TAFE NSW
Technical and Further Education Commission
Manufacturing and Training Division

project assisted by
ETF NSW
Education and Training Foundation

Copyright — Australia 1994   ISBN 0 646 13687 9

Printings — second: 1997, third: 1998, fourth: 1999, fifth: 2000, sixth: 2001, seventh: 2002, eighth: 2003, ninth: 2004, tenth: 2005, eleventh: 2006, twelfth: 2007, thirteenth: 2008, fourteenth: 2009, fifteenth: 2010, sixteenth: 2011, seventeenth: 2013, eighteenth: 2015.

CONTENTS

ROSE SAMUELS is a member of the Faculty of Manufacturing at the Sydney Institute of Technology, TAFE, New South Wales. Her career began in the cutting room of an Australian garment manufacturing company. Since then, in a continuous fourteen-year association with the industry, she has worked in every sector of apparel design and production.

During her six years in vocational education Samuels has taught students, developed training resources and lectured to fashion teaching staff on marking and cutting. She is currently evolving an industry/education liaison program.

Samuels' own training was acquired in Australia and supplemented in the USA. She has conducted formal studies of garment industry work practices in Australia, USA and Hong Kong.

RONNIE HOFFMAN worked for two decades as a journalist, writer and broadcaster in Britain, Ireland and France. He developed a special interest in business affairs.

Moving to Australia in the mid nineteen-eighties he was appointed editor of "Inside Retailing". After two years he set up his own company and began to write, edit and publish magazines and books, including "SewTrade", adopted as the journal of the Clothing and Footwear Institute.

From a background which began in daily newspapers, then moved to radio and television documentaries and on to business magazines, Hoffman has published detailed studies of several industries, a marketing textbook, a variety of training modules and a series of guidebooks for exporters.

A CUT ABOVE THE REST, a basic guide to marker-making and cutting, is Hoffman's third book in this series for the apparel industry. It is the first in collaboration with Samuels. (The first in the series, a quality control guide titled "Tried and Tested" is now in its second printing and still selling steadily. The second, "Hanging By a Thread" a recently published study of sewing threads, has been adopted by many colleges and training bodies in Australasia.)

Like the two books which preceded it in the series, "A Cut Above The Rest" is rich in pracical fact, simple in style and free from jargon. Its approach is to simplify a complex manufacturing process without trivialising it. It is user-friendly.

It has two aims. First it serves the apparel industry as a book of basic instruction. Later retained on the office, studio or workshop, it is a work of reference.

It also serves two levels of readers. In the apparel manufacturing industry it provides everyday working guidance for managers, supervisors and operators. At the training level it is a standard beginners' instruction manual for apprentices and students.

PREFACE

The cutting process cannot be reversed. There is no practical way to re-seal a knife-cut in a fabric.

Though it is the first manufacturing activity in a series, cutting is the point of no return. If the cutting is right, all processes which follow it have a chance to be right. If the cutting is wrong, the problem will persist, and perhaps be multiplied, as the manufacturing process proceeds.

In an industrial cutting-room, the multiplication factor is an ever-present pressure. The worst outcome for one dressmaker, who makes a mistake when cutting one pattern piece from one length of fabric may be one spoiled garment.

In the apparel industry, the cutter is likely to be dealing with hundreds of metres of fabric at any one time. A cutter who activates a knife incorrectly, for whatever reason, may be spoiling a whole week's production — or may be causing the company to miss the season entirely.

"A Cut Above The Rest" aims to explain the process which takes fabric from its arrival in bulk to its departure, in accurately-cut pieces, of the right number, in the right order, at the correct moment, towards sewing machines and assembly. And it offers this explanation in simple terms which are as jargon-free as possible.

The two authors provide a balanced blend of experience. One has spent fourteen years either working as a cutter, or teaching cutting skills to technical students and teachers. The other has spent twenty years as a business journalist, broadcaster and author.

Both received encouragement, support and assistance from the Manufacturing Training Division of TAFE (NSW), from the Australian TCF Industry Training Board (NSW), from the NSW Chamber of Manufactures, from the NSW Education and Training Foundation.

The authors' thanks go to the many people who provided their time and information with generosity and patience.

RS and RH

Australia 1994

In the same series:

TRIED AND TESTED — a basic guide to quality control for the apparel industry

HANGING BY A THREAD — a guide to sewing threads for the apparel industry

FANCY STITCHING — a basic guide to machine embroidery for the apparel industry

WHAT HAPPENS IN THE CUTTING ROOM?

THE MOST EXPENSIVE single component in the average Australian-made garment is the fabric.

The most crucial process in the manufacture of a garment is the cutting. In the cutting room the fabric is received, checked, cut into the appropriate components, and sent on its way to be sewn.

If the cutting room does its job correctly, the components are likely be sewn together with speed and accuracy. But when the cutting room fails, either to deliver the right components of the right shape in the right numbers, or to deliver them at the right time, the remainder of the process is going to slow down or stop completely.

To a garment manufacturer who is competing for a share of the retail market and attempting to be cost-effective, it matters little whether the production process has been slowed or stopped because the cutting was inaccurate or because it was delayed.

In either event the disruption has cost some or all of the manufacturer's profit. And without profit, a garment manufacturer soon ceases to trade.

CUTTING — AN OVERVIEW

THERE ARE EIGHT logical steps within the cutting and marker-making process. From the moment the fabric comes in through the factory door, until it leaves, cut and bundled, ready to be sewn, it is the responsibility of the cutting room and those who work in it.

Here is a brief description of each stage:

1 RECEIPT AND STORAGE — The cutting room usually accepts delivery of all the "piece goods" which come into the manufacturing area. Piece goods include everything required for garment production, such as the fabrics, linings, fusings, trimmings and even accessories. The term does not include papers or items of cutting and marking equipment.

Both the quantity and the quality of inwards goods have to be checked. Then everything has to be stored so that it can easily be found when needed, and so that it will not deteriorate while it is waiting.

2 MARKER MAKING — This is the process of developing a diagram, rather like a jigsaw puzzle, made up from garment pattern pieces. The aim is to produce the best, most efficient and most cost-effective pattern placement.

It must be done within the limitations imposed by the available production equipment and by the nature of the fabric itself. When complete, it will serve as a guide during the process of cutting the fabric into garment component parts.

3 SPREADING — This is the process of laying out the "plies" of fabric on the cutting table. When complete, the stack of plies is usually referred to as "the lay".

The spreader's aim is to create the lay in a manner which permits the maximum possible number of plies to be cut simultaneously into garment components.

4 CUTTING — The process which actually cuts the lay (bulk fabric) into garment component parts is usually known as cutting, but is sometimes referred to as chopping or knifing.

The cutting process may be divided into two main categories:

When the cutter follows the outline and shape of the pattern exactly, immediately producing a garment component part, the process is pattern cutting.

Sometimes a cutter, perhaps when faced with a complicated shape or an unsympathetic fabric, does not follow the exact pattern. Instead he/she allows some extra fabric around it, so that the pieces may be cut later with greater accuracy.

This process is known as block cutting. (See "reblocking" below.)

5 POSITION MARKING — Complete patterns, ready for cutting, are often more than an outline shape. Depending upon style, in addition to an outline, they may contain notches and drillholes. These are guide marks which enable the sewing machinist to align the components accurately when making up the garment.

The process of placing these guide marks (notches and drill holes) on the surface and/or perimeter of the cut garment parts is position marking.

6 REBLOCKING — Plies of fabric which have been block cut (see 4, above) must be spread so that they may be cut again, this time with accuracy. This process is "reblocking".

7 BUNDLING — Once the plies of fabric have been cut, the individual stacks of garment pieces must be sorted (usually by size), identified, then bagged or tied to be made ready for their move towards sewing and assembly.

At this stage, the large bundles from the cutting room may be taken apart and made up into smaller bundles, suitable for distribution to individual sewing machine operators. Both these processes are known as bundling.

It is a matter of some importance that components cut from the same plies should be assembled into the same garment. Inaccurate alignment of plies can lead to the production of second-quality garments.

8 TICKETING — A ticket is needed to identify each bundle. It is important to know what the component is, from which batch of fabric it was cut and for which garment it is destined. All this information should be found on a ticket.

There are two phases of the ticketing process. The first is certainly the responsibility of the cutting room. This takes place after the lay has been cut into garment components.

These components are grouped together, usually by size, bundled and ticketed with the appropriate style number, size and possibly a batch or order number.

The second phase may take place when the bundles of sizes, as described above, are passed on to the person (in the production department of the factory, or perhaps an outside sub-contractor) who is to assemble the components into a garment.

At this stage the bundles may be opened to be re-bundled into smaller quantities for each machinist, then re-ticketed, usually after the components have been further sorted by colour or dyelot. In cases where it is necessary to ensure correct realignment of the pieces from each ply, every component piece may have to be labelled with a detachable sticker. This is a precaution often taken in the manufacture of jeans.

———————————

The continued use of the word "yardage" for fabric supplied in metric measure, can lead to real problems. Many fabric mills in China and India still make and supply fabric in yards. A yard is smaller than a metre. So a delivery of 100 yards of fabric contains only 91.44 metres.

An Australian garment manufacturer who receives a delivery of 3,000 yards of fabric when expecting 3,000 metres is going to be some 260 metres short.

PIECE GOODS – WHERE QUALITY BEGINS

THE QUALITY of a manufactured garment can be no higher than the quality of the materials from which it is made. A garment maker who begins his/her task with imperfect fabric is likely to be creating problems rather than solving them.

In most factories, all piece goods, certainly all fabrics, are delivered to the cutting room. There the fabric is received, checked and stored.

Delivery

In most companies, the cutting room staff would usually be held responsible for carrying out two basic tests when taking delivery of piece goods.

They ensure that every metre of fabric ordered and listed on the delivery docket has actually been delivered. (Even if it is marked and listed in metres, fabric is still often referred to as "yardage".)

The cutting room would also be expected to cast an expert eye over the fabric to find and identify any imperfections.

If, having conducted its tests, the cutting room discovers a shortfall in length and/or quality, a suitable claim must be made against the supplier. Frequently, this claim must be lodged within a fairly short time of the fabric's delivery.

So a good method, plus a sense of urgency, would be part of the basic requirement. It is worth remembering that fabric suppliers are probably going to refute complaints about quantity or quality, once a fabric has been cut.

Some essential details need to be verified when a delivery is made. The delivery dockets should be checked against copies of the original order (to do this the cutting room would usually co-operate with the buying office or production department) to ensure that the goods have been correctly listed and priced. This task could be carried out manually, using files or order books, or increasingly is carried out by making an entry on a computer.

Then the merchandise itself should be checked to ensure that what is listed in the documentation is what has been packed in the parcels, bales, boxes or packages.

For this task it is a good idea to work from a check-list. Then nothing is forgotten.

Begin by examining the outer packing. Is there damage ? Has something been torn, crushed or otherwise distorted ? Are there signs of water or other fluid stains ?

If damage is visible, make certain that the carrier's delivery docket is marked accordingly, before it is signed. If compensation is to be claimed, it may be crucial to establish that the damage occurred before the delivery was made.

Every company will have its own system, of course, but once a trouble-free delivery has been verified, there is likely to be a method for a copy of the delivery docket to find its way to the accounts office so that it may be checked, matched with its appropriate order and invoice, and eventually paid.

Many cutting rooms maintain a stock book to record the details of incoming goods. This might list:

* The date the goods were received
* A brief description of type and quantity
* The name of the supplier
* The purchase order and delivery docket numbers
* The name of the employee making the entry
* Comments such as "packaging torn" or "quantity correct"

If a package is opened and its contents are found to be faulty, the entire contents of the package (sometimes the whole consignment) may have to be kept on one side, and certainly not put into work, until a claim has been lodged.

It is worth noting that not all damage to fabric is caused by poor manufacturers or careless weavers. More than one bale of fine fabric has been damaged by a cutting room employee who opened the package with a blade — which bit too deep.

Storage

People sometimes forget that there are two reasons for storage. One, obviously, is that the merchandise should be kept in good order. The other, sometimes overlooked, is that it should be located quickly and easily.

Good storage, in cutting room terms, means that the fabrics are stacked securely so that everything is protected (including the people who must walk between the stacks) and so that nothing deteriorates through dirt, heat, damp, discoloration, insect contamination or mishandling.

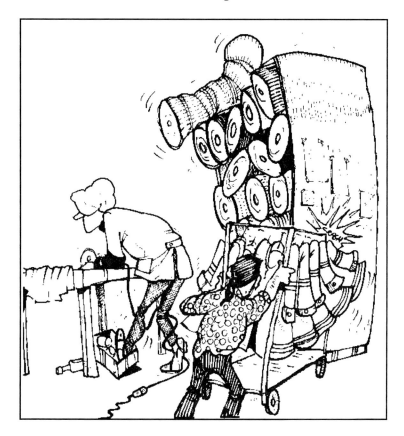

But good storage also means that, through a series of accurate and up-to-date labels and records, everyone knows where everything is, and anyone can lay hands on any piece of any fabric at any time.

Well stored and accurately labelled fabric also means that the regular chore of stocktaking is reduced to a minimum. Today's technology makes life even easier by providing barcode labels which can be instantly recognised by a small electronic "reader" similar to that seen in supermarket checkouts.

The most careful piece of management planning can go suddenly astray if the fabric for the next day's production cannot be found — or if when it is found, it is in an unusable condition.

Here are some basic "good storage" guidelines:

1 Fabric is best stored in groups, according to its type. Ideally, each section, bay, rack or stack should be labelled according to its type.

2 Each piece (or roll) of fabric should carry a ticket which is either visible or available.

3 Every ticket and rack label should carry the fullest possible details: supplier, type, colourways, dyelot, length. Tickets and rack labels should be updated as the fabric is used.

4 The most suitable atmosphere for a fabric store is cool and dry.

5 Direct and unfiltered sunlight can cause fabric to fade.

6 Direct heat on fabric (such as an electric light bulb in contact with the top of a stack) can cause damage. It can also cause a fire.

7 Fabric tears easily. Make certain all storage fixtures are free from nails, sharp edges, splinters, etc.

8 When fabric rolls are stacked, one on the other, it is sensible to criss-cross them. This ensures a more stable stack. It also allows a reasonable air-flow.

9 It is unwise to stack fabrics so that they are touching the floor. Using a stand, pallet or shelf, create a minimum clearance of about 10 cm.

10 Faced or napped fabrics require special attention. When too many are stacked, the weight may damage the lower rolls.

11 Dust can penetrate fabrics and cause damage. Regular dusting is important. Dust extractors are a wise investment.

12 Fabric which is likely to be in storage for more than two or three months should be covered with a dust sheet.

13 Every time fabric is handled, even in the roll, there is a risk of damage or deterioration. The best handling is the least handling.

14 Fabrics which have a natural fibre content (either plant or animal) are only safe when stored in an area which has been sprayed with insecticide.

15 Fabrics can absorb odours quickly, but tend to release them slowly. Strong-smelling substances are best kept well away from stored fabrics.

Fabric inspection

Most apparel manufacturers are not equipped to carry out laboratory tests on the fabrics they use. They must rely, to a great extent, on the tests carried out and the guarantees given by the fabric manufacturers and supliers.

Some of the more simple tests, of washability, dyefastness, colourfastness and shrinkage for example, are well within the scope of many garment manufacturers. *

For the average cutting room, fabric inspection has two principal functions. These are:

1 To ensure that, within reasonable limits, the fabric supplied conforms with the original order. In simple terms, this means that the fabric will do what it is expected to do. If it is not to specification, it may be returned to the supplier.

2 To detect and identify damaged sections of an otherwise acceptable fabric. The damaged portions are marked and

measured so that the cutter will not use them and (if the amount damaged goes beyond acceptable limits) so that the supplier may be approached for a price adjustment.

To assist with the process of cloth inspection there are machines and mechanical aids in all grades of cost and complexity.

A basic inspection machine, which in fact is the type most commonly used in the industry, performs two functions.

It checks the length of the fabric piece by rolling it through a wheeled measuring device. At the same time it passes the fabric over a light table so that it may be inspected for faults in manufacture.

All fabric, but particularly high-priced fabric, should be checked on arrival. Essentially, the inspector is looking for manufacturing (or printing or dyeing or weaving) faults, for shortages in length and for variations in width.

How much time the inspection should take will depend on the value of the fabric. A costly cloth will require a generous amount of time and a careful appraisal. When dealing with an inexpensive cloth, however, a moment will come when the value of the fabric "saved" by an inspection will become less than the cost of the inspector's time.

Sampling

A relatively small quantity of fabric, supplied so that a garment manufacturer may make up sample garments to show to his/her customers, is usually known in the industry as "sampling".

When a sample has been made up and shown, the garment manufacturer is able to calculate the total amount of fabric required and order it from the fabric supplier.

Unfortunately, it sometimes happens that the fabric supplied for the bulk order is less, in quality and/or weight, than the fabric supplied for sampling.

Many garment manufacturers have at some time experienced this shortfall in weight or quality. It could mean that, if this fabric is used, the garments delivered may never reach the quality achieved by the sample.

To ensure that this situation does not occur, it makes good sense when ordering fabric to quote both the article number and the weight (usually shown as weight per specific length) on the order. It is also sensible to weigh a measured length of fabric to ensure that when the bulk fabric is delivered, the correct ratio has been maintained.

An accurate set of weighing scales is a useful quality control tool to have available in the cutting room. In days gone by, when

a great deal of "gents suiting" fabric was being made by British woollen mills, there were companies which would specialise in cloth stretching.

A length of woollen cloth, having been weighed and officially indelibly stamped as being a specified number of ounces to the yard, would be taken to a cloth stretcher who, with steam, pressing and large hot rollers pulling in opposite directions, would magically "create" an additional suit length on each bolt of cloth.

The stretched fabric would have retained its stamped verification. Thus it would have retained its price. But it would have been reduced in weight by perhaps an ounce in the yard. A simple weighing scale could have revealed all.

Weight is a good guide to fabric length. It is particularly useful when handling a less expensive fabric which might not justify the spending of the costly employee time required to measure it, metre by metre. Once the width has been checked, a set length (perhaps ten metres) can be weighed.

This weight becomes the basis for a calculation of the length of fabric rolls or bolts when delivered. Of course, the weight of the wrapping and the tube or board round which the fabric has been rolled must first be deducted from the total.

* Several simple fabric tests are listed in the book: "Tried and Tested – a basic guide to quality control in the apparel industry" published by Publishing and Production Projects Pty Ltd, PO Box 1000, Potts Point, NSW 2011.

CUTTING ORDERS

THE CREATION of a garment begins with a cutting order. A cutting order contains two basic elements.

It is firstly the authorisation to start the process which manufactures garments from bulk fabric. It is secondly the manufacturing company's record of which garments in which style and sizes are to be cut from which fabric.

Usually each cutting order relates only to one style and fabric. But most orders call for a specified number of garments, in a specified number of sizes, in that style.

There is no special limit to the number of garments described in a single cutting order. In some cases, the number may be so high that one "spread" (see Chapter six) is not sufficient.

In larger companies, the cutting order is likely to be produced and authorised by the production manager. In smaller companies, the rule is that there is no rule.

Components of a cutting order

Because there can be a huge variation in the type and number of production control systems followed by companies, there can be an equally wide variation in the type of information recorded on a cutting order.

Some orders might include a great deal of detail which extends beyond fabric and cutting into manufacture and delivery. Others might contain cross-references to other cutting orders — either for other styles for the same client or of the same style for another client.

But whatever its overall content, a cutting order can be expected to contain such basic information as:

* order number
* date of order
* fabric to be cut
* style number

* quantity of sizes
* variety of colours
* date required for completion
* special requirements (fabrics, patterns etc)
* estimated fabric quantity (from costing)
* space for actual fabric quantity

Most companies expect the actual quantity of fabric used to be less (or certainly no more) than the estimated quantity on which the garment's cost calculation was based.

In addition to the above information, a cutting order often includes such information as:

* quantity of fabric issued with order
* fabric swatches
* handling, manufacturing and/or despatch details
* space for cutter's remarks and signature

What is perhaps the most vital piece of information is not recorded on the cutting order, but should (in most companies, must) accompany the cutting order to the cutting room. It is a correct sample garment.

An accurate sample of the garment to be cut is an extremely valuable insurance against possible errors. It is like the proverbial picture, which is said to be "worth a thousand words".

In the mind of the cutter, a sight of the sample can clarify the requirement exactly. It can ensure that the wrong fabric is not cut and that all the necessary pieces are included. It reinforces information with understanding.

In addition, it allows the cutter's experienced eye to judge whether the designer was making the best possible use of the fabric or whether an identical effect could be achieved using less fabric and/or a more economic operation.

Whether it creates potential savings or forestalls possible mistakes, a sample which accompanies a cutting order almost invariably pays its way. And if either the cutting or the assembly is to be carried out by a sub-contractor working away from direct supervision, a sample is of crucial importance

Step by step

In order to produce a cutting order, information must be gathered from a variety of sources. Speed and accuracy are important.

The first information comes from the sales department (or people, or person). All customers' orders are compiled so that a total requirement for styles, sizes and delivery dates may be calculated.

This same information is extremely useful to both marketing and design staff within the company. And the more up-to-date the information, the more useful it is.

In many instances, to acquire fashionable fabrics, a manufacturer must place early orders with fabric suppliers. The manufacturer must speculate by ordering fabric in advance of any indication from wholesalers and retailers of their requirements.

The amount of fabric in a garment manufacturer's stock, plus the amount due for delivery, will impose limits on the number of garments a company can manufacture and sell.

The compiled customers' orders will indicate when such a limit is being reached (or worse, when it has been overstepped). Up-to-date information will allow the fabric stock position to be monitored with accuracy.

Knowing that the fabric stocks are running out, the company will be able to take the necessary action, which might be:

* re-ordering the fabric, if it is available

* withdrawing a style from sale, if necessary

* offering customers an alternate fabric

* (when all else fails) telling customers that part of an order cannot be filled.

The reasons behind the compilation of orders are simple. The aim is to cut, at any one time, as many garments of a particular style as is practical. This ensures that the cutting room is being as cost-effective as it can be.

Thus a single cutting order is likely to contain a batch of smaller buying orders from a number of different customers.

If a cutting order has been well designed, it can travel with the cut component parts through the cutting and sewing processes. Then it can be used as a check-list by the despatch department as it makes up orders for individual customers.

This compilation, handling and reconstruction of orders is something at which the computer excels. There are now several programs which, given the necessary data, can produce all the required information at the required times.

In addition, there are programs which assist the production manager and the cutter in planning their output so that the best possible use is made of cutting room and sewing room time, producing an optimum balance of fabrics and styles.

Every company will have its own approach to this set of problems. And, hopefully, most company managers will have an open-minded approach to the possibility of change.

But for all companies, the decision-making process should aim to create a balance between the apparently conflicting influences of customers' orders, delivery dates, production speeds, availability of fabrics and the influence of market forces.

What to cut and when to cut it is a decision which, above all others, must be made in the light of the most recent information — even if, to the production manager's annoyance, a whole set of earlier decisions must be modified.

―――――――――――――

THE MARKER

What and why

A "MARKER" is a plan which shows the most economic layout which can be achieved, using the pattern pieces of a specific garment and working with a specific fabric. Anyone making a marker must consider many factors, from pattern shapes to fabric grainlines.

The marker-maker is also influenced by the number of different sizes to be made of a particular style of garment.

In its simplest form, a marker is a plan prepared (in actual size, not usually to scale) on a large sheet of paper. The paper is laid flat and marked with the width of the fabric to be used.

The pattern pieces are sorted according to size of garment and fabric used, then placed on the flat paper and within the fabric width as marked, with the straight grainlines of the patterns parallel to the selvedge of the fabric, while carefully following the patternmaker's cutting instructions.

A suitable and economic layout is established, usually by the trial-and-error method of shuffling the pieces about. The outlines of the pattern pieces are then drawn on the marker paper, with a pen or pencil.

An additional factor is introduced into the process when the fabric carries a weave pattern, a print or (like velvet) a nap. Sometimes a fabric feature must be matched on each component part when the garment is made up. Sometimes a specific segment of the fabric's design must be made to appear on a specific part of the garment. Sometimes both are required.

In such cases a marker-maker may find it simpler to mark the pattern pieces directly onto the fabric to make what is sometimes known as a "cloth marker" and which is used in the same way as a paper marker.

Eventually, taking each factor into account, all the pattern pieces are marked-in. The area covered by the pieces will establish the length of the lay. So the fabric is laid up accordingly and the marker attached to the top of the lay using clamps, staples or weights. The job is then ready for cutting.

A simple sample

When a cutting order is passed to the person who will make the marker, it is ideally accompanied by a made-up sample of the garment to be cut. This sample should be made accurately in the fabric from which the style is to be produced.

The presence of a good sample answers almost all the marker-maker's questions about pattern layout and possible variations in fabric print, stripe or other design. When there are several options open to the marker-maker, the sample garment indicates the most suitable.

When customers place orders, they expect a particular finish and appearance from a particular garment at a particular price. A mistake in the marker-making process might mean that the garment cannot be made at all, or cannot be produced economically, or when produced it differs from the garment which was originally ordered.

Such a mistake often leads to the production of garments which customers find unacceptable.

Pattern requirements

Many patterns carry detailed cutting instructions. They should be read and followed carefully by the marker-maker. Not every pattern-maker is a good communicator and an instruction could be open to more than one interpretation.

When there is doubt, the situation can usually be clarified by a careful examination of the sample. Then, though the instruction may not be evident, the objective is clear.

Sometimes the pattern-maker might write: "Cut PAIR self."

This means that the pattern must be turned over when being marked-in, even if the fabric is being spread "face to face". The marker must always have "paired" pattern pieces, if the cutting instructions require it.

Occasionally a pattern-maker will write: "Cut 2 self" when in fact a pair is required. It is the marker-maker's responsibility to check the source or the sample and to remove all doubt.

Similarly, it may be necessary to clarify: "*RSU*" which usually means: "Right Side Up". In such cases the marker-maker might expect to mark-in the pattern with the writing side uppermost, and to have the fabric laid-up with its face side uppermost.

Grain lines

The grainline on a pattern piece is an instruction, to the marker-maker, on how to place the pattern on the fabric in order to achieve the desired effect.

The pattern grainline should always be laid parallel to the selvedge of the fabric. (The straight "grain" of a fabric may be expected to run lengthwise along it.)

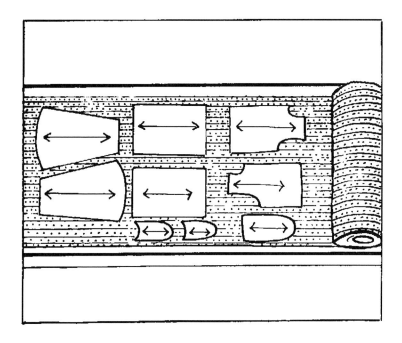

Sometimes, to take advantage of a fabric print or to achieve better fabric utilisation, a marker-maker may mark pieces "crosswise straight grain", which is at right-angles to the "lengthwise straight grain" direction. Ideally, all the garment pieces should be cut on the same grain, whether lengthwise or crosswise.

When a marker-maker wishes to mark patterns on crosswise straight grain, and all sample garments have been made-up on lengthwise straight grain, a new sample (using the new grainline) should be cut and made-up for the patternmaker's approval before another step is taken.

Very occasionally, perhaps for a significant saving, a few pieces of a garment may be marked on a different grainline from the rest. This is possible when pieces, such as fused facings, are not critical to the garment's appearance.

Notches

Notches — which are also known a nicks — are balance points marked on the edges of garment component parts to assist in the identification and assembly of the pieces during the manufacturing process.

As the marker-maker traces a line around the pattern pieces, the notch positions should be marked. The most useful (and generally accepted) method for indicating a notch's position on a marker is to draw something resembling a capital "T". The notch is marked as a line, drawn inwards from (and at right angles to) the edge.

The crossbar drawn on the notch serves three purposes:

1 It indicates the depth to which the notches are to be cut

2 It draws the cutter's attention to the notch (which is important but may be overlooked)

3 It identifies a notch on a pattern which, say during tracing, has acquired a few accidental extra lines.

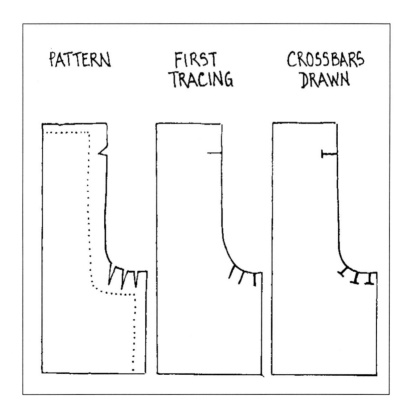

Drillholes

Some patterns contain drillholes. These are used by the machinist during assembly. The marker-maker is required to transfer the drill-holes from the pattern pieces to the marker.

They should then be circled to draw the cutter's attention to them. Additional care is required when dealing with garments on which there are paired patterns.

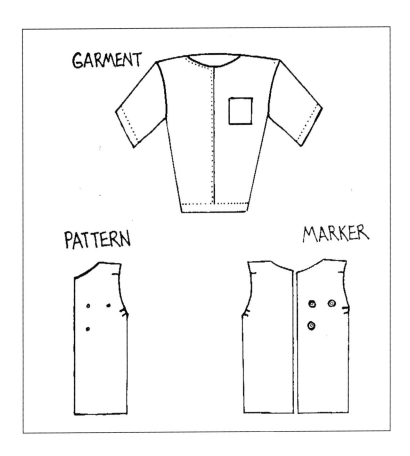

Often drillholes are marked to identify the position of a pocket or tab on a garment. But the detail may be required on one side of the garment only. Thus there may be a need for a matched pair of fronts, with drillholes for a pocket or tab on one side only.

If the fabric has only one "right" side, it will have to be laid-up face side uppermost. If spread "face to face", half the resulting garments would have the pocket on the right, and half would have the pocket on the left.

THE MARKER

How it is made

BEFORE MAKING a marker it is a good idea to ensure that there is enough fabric to complete the cutting order. Bearing in mind that fabric manufacturers can make mistakes, verify the length of each roll (unless this was done when the rolls were delivered) by checking all the labels and by actually measuring at least one roll.

Then check the width of each roll. The narrowest roll width is the one on which to base all calculations.

To find it, simply open the narrowest roll at its narrowest part and measure the distance from the inside of the selvedge on one side to the inside of the selvedge on the other side. Bear in mind that a fabric roll which is 115 centimetres wide might have only 100 or 112 centimetres of "usable" fabric.

The first mark

Open a roll of paper. To make a marker you will need to reproduce on the paper the exact width of usable fabric. So, measuring from one edge of the roll, draw a line along the length of the paper, parallel to that edge, which exactly equals the usable fabric width.

From this line and at a right angle to it, square off the end of the paper by drawing a line across it.

Sorting

Sort the pattern pieces. First sort the sized pattern pieces according to the fabric needed. For example: there might be the "self" fabric, which is the main fabric used in the garment. There might also be a second "contrast" fabric. In addition there might be a fusing and/or a lining to be marked and cut.

Then sort them according to the size of the garments to be made. It is usual to mark-in only one size at a time. Separating the sizes in this way makes it easier to lay and cut the pieces without having to make more garments than the order requires.

Mixing sizes

Having discovered in an earlier paragraph that ". . . separating the sizes makes it easier . . ." the marker-maker soon discovers that the easiest method is not necessarily the most cost-effective method.

There are occasions when, in order to achieve efficiencies and economies, certain sizes are "mixed" and are marked-in together.

For example, suppose a cutting order reads:

sizes -   8   10   12   14
quantity required - 100   200   200   100.

A marker-maker occasionally handles a cutting order where, as in the order above, the quantities required for some sizes are identical. In such instances there is an opportunity to mix the sizes when marking-in the pieces.

Provided the different sizes are carefully identified, the ability to mix in this way usually allows for considerable savings of fabric — and therefore of money. The same number of garments is produced, without skimping in any way, from a much smaller amount of fabric.

So great are the savings, in fact, that sometimes it makes good commercial sense to add a few garments to an order, and to cut "stock" (or unordered) garments. If the garment is popular, the few additional units should be sold with no great effort. Meanwhile the savings made by marking-in some sizes together are of benefit to the whole order.

Stepping

When starting to mark-in the pattern pieces, it is good practice to begin with the size which has been ordered in the smallest numbers and to work towards the sizes which have been ordered in the largest numbers. This allows the fabric spreader to arrange what is called a "step lay".

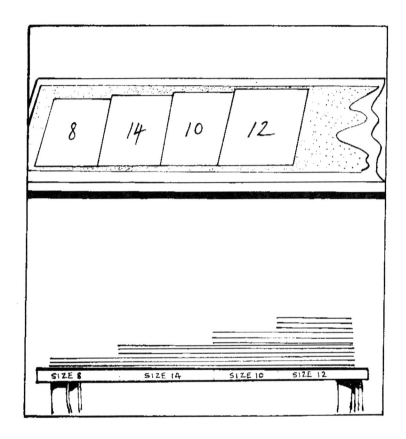

Layout

Taking all the various factors into consideration, the marker-maker will arrange and rearrange the pattern pieces until the most economic layout (still often called the best yardage) is achieved.

If the marker-maker sees an opportunity to move one or more pattern pieces without increasing the usage of fabric, it makes good sense to arrange them so that when the cutting machine completes the cut on one piece, it is on line and pointing in the right direction to move straight to the next piece. A marker-maker can create a layout which saves time and prevents inaccuracies on the cutting table.

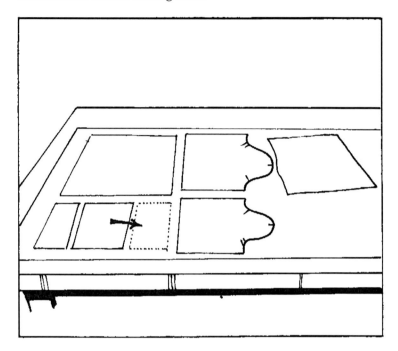

With most fabrics, the pattern pieces may touch, but not overlap when being arranged. The exception is jersey, which needs a small space between the pieces. Jersey tends to shrink away from the cut-line as each piece is cut.

Marking

As each pattern piece is being marked-in, it should be held down with a weight. A movement will create an inaccuracy.

The pieces of each size, the contrast fabrics, linings and interfacings are marked as required. Each pattern piece outlined should carry some sort of code which can identify it and allow it, after cutting, to be grouped together with all the other components of the same size.

Checking

Once the marker is complete, there are three checks to be made.

1 Count — Hold up the sample garment provided with the cutting order and count the number of pieces (two fronts, one back, two sleeves, etc) it contains. Then count the number of pieces marked-in. If the two numbers are not the same, start to worry.

2 Look — If any of the components were to be cut in matched pairs, ensure that the pattern pieces are correctly turned over when being marked-in.

3 Calculate — Measure the yardage (the fabric required) for the whole marker.

For example: if a four-size marker (containing sizes 8, 10, 12 and 14) measured 13.20 metres, the average for one size would be a quarter of 13.20 metres, which is 3.30 metres.

This calculation has revealed the "production yardage" which is the actual amount of fabric to be used when making the garments. It should be checked against the "costing yardage" which was the estimated amount of fabric to be used.

The production figure should not exceed the costing figure. In fact, it would be better if it were slightly lower, using a little less fabric than at first estimated.

A big variation in the wrong (higher) direction could mean that the garment would be produced and sold at a loss. If this is the case, it should be brought to the attention of someone with the authority to decide whether to go ahead, to cancel the order, to vary the style, to reduce the yardage, to substitute another fabric, or to take whatever steps may be taken.

Splices

"Splice positions" need to be indicated on the sides of the marker. A splice position represents a point where fabric may be overlapped to allow a fault to be cut from the fabric.

The fault may be an area within the bulk of the fabric where it is less than perfect, or it may be the unevenness at the end of a roll. The splice allows these problems to be solved with minimal waste.

Splice positions are best when marked on the marker and also marked on paper placed on the table beneath the lay.

There are two types of splice: the straight-line and the interlock.

The straight-line splice is marked, as might be expected, by a straight line across the marker's width.

It indicates a place where end-of-pattern pieces butt together (meet edge-to-edge) on each side of the line. For example, where a size changes, the spreader would mark a single line on the table

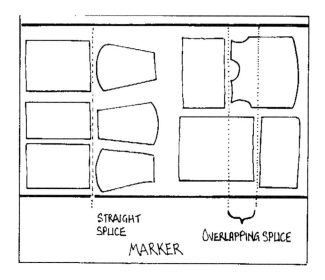

and overlap the fabric by about 5 cm (2 ins) on either side of the indicated splice position.

The interlock splice is marked by crossed diagonal lines.

It indicates a place where end-of-pattern pieces do not butt. Instead, they overlap. These splices have a beginning and an

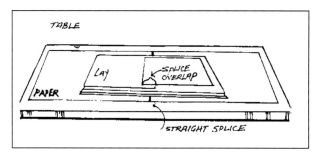

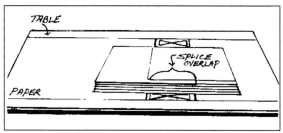

ending so they must be marked with two lines. To avoid possible confusion (one of the two lines may be mistaken for a straight-line splice) the two lines are joined by crossed diagonal lines. A similar 5cm (2 ins) safety extension is required around this splice.

Papers in the cutting room

The process of marker-making requires patterns to be outlined or traced onto paper. There are several types of paper regularly used in the cutting room, for marking and for other purposes.

SPOT AND CROSS is white paper, supplied on a roll, printed all over either with blue numbers or blue spots and crosses. Almost invariably the printing forms a grid with a 2 cm spacing.

The grid enables the marker-maker to align pattern pieces with speed and accuracy. This can create considerable savings of time. But printed paper is far more costly than plain paper. For some jobs, and in some companies the cost of spot and cross is prohibitive.

UNDERLAY paper is a roll of brown paper which has one shiny side and one dull side. It is often used for marker-making. It is also frequently used under the lay.

With its shiny side next to the table and its dull (and less slippery) side against the fabric, it facilitates the movement of portions of the lay, after cutting.

INTERLEAVING is a light paper of tissue weight. It is principally used to make separations in the lay.

For example it might be inserted between fabric plies which originate from different dye lots. By keeping them separate, after cutting, the manufacturer ensures that all components used in the assembly of a garment are from a single dye lot and from the same ply.

SELF-CARBONATING paper serves a purpose similar to office carbon paper, or the paper found in duplicate order books. It is used in the making of copies.

By placing self-carbonating paper under the paper used to make the marker, and by making the pattern outlines on the marker with a hard-point pen, an exact copy is automatically produced.

Marker copying

It is good practice to keep a copy of all markers. If a garment is successful and a second cutting is required, a copy marker is available.

If problems arise and a component is missing, or incorrectly shaped, a copy of the original marker will verify exactly which pieces have (or have not) been cut.

Apart from self-carbonating paper, copies can be made:

* mechanically – copied to full scale by a machine which might use carbon, spirit, pressure or photography

* on disk – computer-controlled marker-making and grading systems are becoming increasingly common.

The computer

Once the province of the extra-large company with the huge production schedule, computer systems are now becoming increasingly popular with medium and smaller companies.

As computer systems themselves adapt to the new small-company market, and operate for shorter runs with increasingly user-friendly programs, so some of the smaller manufacturers become convinced that the speed and covenience associated with computer control is worth the additional financial outlay.

Using a computer workstation, patterns can be created on-screen, scanned or copied and digitised into a system. They can be graded on-screen by a ready-written program and the resultant patterns used to create markers.

Once an operator has been trained and has built enough experience to become familiar with the system, he/she can achieve excellent results.

There is an additional advantage. The pattern and the marker can be stored on disk and recalled whenever necessary.

Many Australian garment manufacturers, some of them quite small in size, are discovering the advantages of computers to their production.

Computers can carry out a great many design, marking and cutting tasks with enormous speed, accuracy and efficiency. In the rights hands, a computer can undertake a huge workload.

But computer systems do not necessarily suit every company's requirements. In addition, a computer cannot be expected to solve every problem with which it comes into contact.

A computer does not have artificial intelligence. It is no more than a clever tool and its products will be only as good as its operator. If there is a "magic wand" of computerised design it is to be found in the training and experience of the staff members who are using it.

SPREADING

WHEN USED in the context of clothing manufacture, spreading is the process of "laying up" in a particular manner the plies or layers of fabric onto the cutting table.

The process is usually carried out along generally agreed and accepted lines. However, not only will each company have its own methods, but sometimes each cutting order will call for a slightly different approach to the spread.

Basic steps

Once cut, a fabric cannot be glued together. So the preparation for the cutting process is an opportunity for another series of checks to make certain that the right fabric is being cut into the right shapes by the right method.

The spreader should check the fabric against the cutting order and the sample garment. If all is as it should be, the spreader will then sequence the fabric rolls so that the narrowest fabric will be laid-up last, thus arriving on the top of the lay.

The spreader must be familiar with company policies and instructions concerning the spreading of various fabrics. Company policies vary greatly and tend to be influenced by the grade, price and style of the garment being produced.

The length of the marker, the splice positions and the places where one size ends and another begins are then marked on a piece of paper. The next move is to attach this paper securely to the cutting table.

If an automatic spreading machine is to be used, this is the moment to place the stops for the machine in the required position. Setting the stops is a job calling for care and accuracy. If the stops are placed wrongly, (and it matters little whether the length of the spread is too great or to small) the result is costly and wasteful.

Regardless of variation in their approach to spreading, most companies agree that the selvedge of the first fabric ply will be laid carefully parallel to the edge of the table. As each successive ply is laid upon it, this edge will be scrupulously matched to build a straight, exact and vertical stack.

Because fabric width may (and probably will) vary considerably, the selvedges on the other edge will be distinctly uneven. Provided there is a good edge to work with, the uneven edge will matter not at all.

The length of fabric which is spread, or to put it another way, the number of plies, or to put it yet another way, the height of the lay, is determined by one or more factors.

The first factor is the number of garments ordered. A well-run cutting room will not lay-up less than a number calculated to be cost-effective. It is worth remembering that the set-up costs remain, however many (or few) pieces are subsequently cut.

The second set of factors are the limitations imposed by the blade height of the available cutting machinery. Depending upon the type of cutting machine to be used, there will be a maximum number of plies which must not be exceeded.

The third factor concerns the fabric itself. Some fabrics are slippery and the lay would be unstable if stacked beyond a certain height, though the machine might cope with more. Other fabrics (such as denim) are difficult to cut so the height of the lay is limited by the ability of the blade.

But whatever the limitations, the spreader always has a simple objective. He/she should produce a lay in which each ply lies perfectly flat, without tension.

Pre-folded or tubular fabric has its obvious spreading requirements. Otherwise fabric can be laid:

* face to face - in which each pair of fabric plies is spread with the faces (or right sides) together

* face up - in which each fabric ply is spread with its face (or right side) upwards

* face down - in which each fabric ply is spread with its face (or right side) down.

Once the lay is complete, the marker can be placed on the top. The marker may have to be cut in one or more places to accommodate a step lay (different sizes, different heights).

When the marker is in position, it is useful to place a ruler across the width, then to run it along the length of the lay. Thus any air which may have become trapped between paper and fabric is expelled.

There are any number of methods regularly used to ensure that the marker adheres to the top of the lay. Everyone has a favourite, which may vary according to conditions and fabrics. In cutting-rooms across the country can be found pins, staples, clamps, weights and spray-on adhesives.

But if tape has been used during preparation to attach any paper to the cutting table, it should be removed before cutting begins.

Good management plays a significant part in good spreading and cutting. The orders passing through the cutting room should resemble trains passing through a well-run station.

As soon as a lay is complete it should be cut, bundled and moved on so that the cutting table is available for the next job. As one order is being handled, the team should be making the next one ready. Without a smooth flow of work, profit will rapidly disappear.

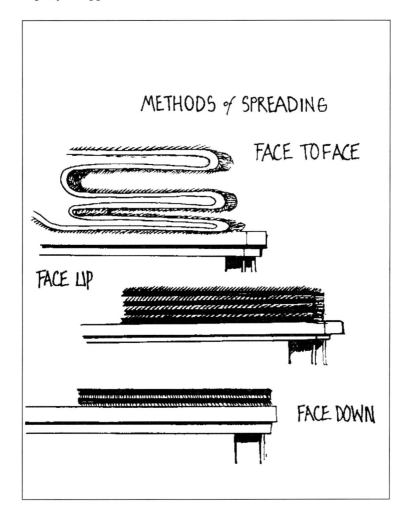

Types of spreading

Manual spreading, the most basic method, usually requires a team of spreaders. The fabric roll will either be placed on a stand at the end of the cutting table, or it will be unrolled for each "run".

A team, usually of two spreaders working on opposite sides of the table, will walk the end of the fabric down the length of the table. There, the end will be carefully aligned and secured, usually with weights.

As the two-person team returns to the end of the table from which they began, they will smooth and align the newly-laid ply as they go. This system can be used for a face-up, face-down or face-to-face lay.

Machine spreading is today's most commonly used method. The wide variety of machines now on the market provides a considerable variation in degrees of automation. Most machines, however, require only a single operator.

The simplest spreading machine runs up and down the length of the cutting table, laying the fabric and folding each ply over its predecessor. This produces a lay which is face-to-face, with the fabric running alternately in each direction.

When it is necessary for the fabric all to run in the same direction, a turnable machine is required. The turnable spreading machine is able to rotate the fabric roll.

A good spreader will acquire an understanding of the cutter's skills and the cutter's problems. Some cutting difficulties can be resolved at the spreading stage.

For example, the baseplate of some cutting machines can occasionally disturb the lowest fabric ply. This is particularly true when heavy fabrics are being cut. For almost every job the spreader places a layer of paper strategically under the lowest ply, so that the baseplate can slide smoothly and safely between paper and table, leaving the fabric undistorted.

Spreading machines

There are three main types of spreading machine in current use. There are, of course, different models within each category. In addition, there are many different attachments which can be acquired and used.

The first type of spreading machine is the simple manual. It is hand propelled by its operator. It uses neither stops nor clamps at the end of the lay. The operator must stop at each end to fold and/or weight the fabric as required.

The second type of machine is the semi-automatic. Though it is hand propelled by its operator, this machine uses stops at the beginning and end of the lay. While its performance depends on the task it is set, the semi-automtaic is generally accepted to be twice as fast as the manual machine.

The third type, the electronic machine, is completely automatic. Once loaded with fabric and set, the machine will travel between the stops and, at each end, will raise the clamp, fold the fabric accurately, reclamp it, and return.

At almost every task, the fully automatic spreading machine is by far the fastest.

There are many attachments for spreading machines. Not every attachment can be used on every machine. Among the most commonly used attachments are:

* a turntable, which allows the spreader to lay fabric in one direction (essential for napped fabric, such as velvet)

* direct drive, which feeds the fabric onto the table, rather than allowing it to be pulled off the roll. Even a light pull on some fabrics can create tensions and distortions. But in use, the machine requires a complex and time-consuming threading process. So it is usually unsuitable for short production runs.

* end cutters, which can slice through the fabric far more swiftly and accurately than the most skilled manual operators.

New developments

With so much of the apparel industry's technology based on electronics and the microchip, the pace of development is rapid. New approaches and improved methods are being announced all the time.

Upgrading packages are offered to owners of existing machinery. Revised and improved models are offered to those seeking something new. People who work in the cutting-room and wish to keep themselves well informed and up-to-date need to maintain regular contact with the machinery makers and suppliers, and to appraise the technical press and publications.

Among the more recently announced cutting-room advances are:

* cutting machine loading systems which make it even more simple to handle rolls of fabric

* cradle-feed systems which eliminate the need to suspend fabric rolls from a bar passing through the centre

* extra-large roll-handling devices which can accommodate a roll of fabric weighing up to 750 kg (1,650 lbs)

* fully automatic spreading machines, which, once set up, can take the task from start to finish

* computer control of both marker-making and cutting operations

* continued increases in the speed and accuracy of all processes

* sensors which can detect faults in fabric and/or variations in width

* spreading machines fitted with a platform on which the operator can ride swiftly along the length of the table.

As machinery suppliers compete for garment manufacturers' business, the list of developments and innovations continues (and will continue) to grow. It makes good sense to ask regularly: "What's new ?"

CUTTING –
WHAT, WHERE AND HOW

What is cutting?

THE CUTTING process begins with bulk fabric and ends with a specified number of garment component parts.

The fabric is cut into pieces. Depending upon the number of pieces to be cut, the type of fabric, the style of garment and the available facilities in the cutting room, the action of cutting is carried out by:

* a manual cutting machine which is usually a freestanding, hand-operated, small device with either a straight or a circular blade

* the die cutting process which uses mechanical pressure to push a die through fabric plies

* a band knife which is a constantly rotating ribbon-like blade against which the blocks of fabric are pressed

* computerised cutting which requires a computer control mechanism to operate a blade, a laser or a water-jet

* a servo cutter which is similar to a freestanding machine, but is supported on a moving arm.

The cutting table

Every production activity in the cutting room centres around the cutting table. The table plays a crucial role. If the cutting room is to work effectively, the cutting table must be:

* of a height, width and strength which will accommodate the fabric being used

* fitted with a table-top which has a totally smooth surface, free from open joints, splinters and snags

* able to bear the moving weight of fabric and machines without movement (which usually requires a steel frame)

* suitable for dismantling for removal, and suitable for an occasional addition of extra table-top

* strengthened along one edge (and possibly fitted with a metal track) for the use of a spreading machine.

When choosing a cutting table, it makes good sense to select the best which available money can buy. Most cutters agree that, over the life of a cutting table, a combination of quality and durability will more than compensate for a relatively high initial outlay.

High quality equipment in the cutting-room will usually pay its way by providing long-term trouble-free service.

Cutting-room machinery

There must be very few cutting rooms which are not equipped with some sort of machinery. A cutting machine is a basic tool of the garment industry.

In reasonably expert hands, one machine in a cutting-room can be expected to produce enough garment parts to keep at least 50 and perhaps 100 machinists working. So the selection and suitability of a cutting machine is of great importance.

But not all machines are good at all tasks. Such considerations as fabric type, pattern piece shape, speed of operation and standards required are part of the selection process.

ROTARY cutting machines are among the fastest available. Because of their design they are best suited to cutting straight lines and gradual curves. The blade is circular in shape. This imposes limitations.

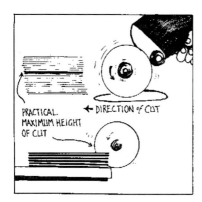

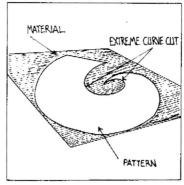

A rotary machine cannot cut a lay, the depth of which is greater than the radius (half the width, measured at the widest point)) of the blade. The most commonly-used rotary cutting machines may be expected to cope with a lay of between 2.5 cm (1 inch) and 9.0 cm (3.5 inches) in depth.

There is a further limitation. The circular blade does not present its cutting edge at the same point to every ply of fabric in a lay.

So the cutting of notches and corners may cause problems.

If the blade is pushed into the edge of the lay to cut a notch, the cut at the lowest point of the lay is not as deep as the cut at the highest point.

A clean cut at a corner presents similar problems. Without overcutting, the cutter would usually have to stop short of the corner, and finish with shears.

STRAIGHT BLADE cutting machines are better suited than rotary blades to dealing with lays of greater height, and patterns with sharper curves and inward-facing corners.

There are a number of factors which must be taken into consideration when a straight-blade cutting machine is being selected. As with all other cutting machines, the performance expected and the fabric selected are the principal influences. But there are many others.

BLADE HEIGHT can be anything from 10.0 cm (4 inches) to 35.0 cm (14 inches). Obviously, the more plies of fabric which can be cut at one time, the less costly the process. But some fabrics do not lend themselves to accurate handling unless the lay is relatively low.

The general rule for freestanding cutting machines is: the shorter the blade the more accurate the cut pieces.

MOTOR SPEED is usually categorised simply as "high" and "low". A high-speed motor can be expected to cut more plies in slightly less time. It can also be expected to be less easily controlled and turned than a low-speed cutter.

There is another consideration. Heat is generated by the cutting action. And the greater the speed of the blade, the greater the amount of heat it produces. So fabrics containing synthetic and/or thermoplastic fibres may begin to melt and fuse when being cut at high speeds.

MACHINE WEIGHT tends to be a matter of personal selection. Naturally, a strongly-made and robust machine is likely to be heavier than a flimsy lightweight. But there is a limit to everyone's strength when a machine has to be lifted and pushed, with accuracy, for a whole working day. The answer may be a compromise.

THE LIFT OR STROKE of a blade is the vertical distance it travels. As a general rule, the longer the stroke the faster the action. But the rule continues: the shorter the stroke, the slower but the smoother the action.

BASEPLATE SIZE tends to vary, reflecting the different approaches and theories of the different machine designers and manufacturers. Essentially, a freestanding machine needs a baseplate which will support it, during operation, with enough stability to make it safe and accurate, but with enough manoeuvrability to make it adaptable.

It is worth noting that a servo machine, which is similar to a freestanding machine, but has its weight supported on a moving arm, is able to operate with a very small baseplate. For this reason it reacts very well to the lightest touch.

BLADE TYPES tend to fall into five main categories, though as with most mechanical devices there are many minor variations and frequent new (though not necessarily better) approaches.

In simple terms, blades may be:

* straight   – for general cutting
* waved   – for plastics
* notched   – for backed plastics
* saw   – for canvas
* serrated   – for hard cottons.

LUBRICATION during the cutting process can be an absolute essential or a mild advantage, depending on the blade, the fabric and the type of operation. Usually lubricant is fed in varying degrees through an attachment. But, as the cutting action requires a certain amount of abrasion between the knife edge and the fabric, the degree of lubrication is less than easy to determine.

SHARPENING BELTS are available for straight-blade cutting machines. These are small belts of emery paper which are fitted to the sharpening attachments usually found on each side of a cutting machine's blade. The belts rotate when triggered. Cutters will sharpen the blades regularly during cutting.

There are four grades of sharpening belt: rough, coarse, medium and fine. The grade is selected according to the weight of the fabric being cut. (The machine supplier can offer expert advice when shown a fabric sample.) There are also special waterproof sharpening belts which can be used while a cutting machine is also using a lubricant.

SHARPENING BLOCKS will do for circular-blade cutting machines what sharpening belts (see above) will do for straight-blade cutting machines.

Special-purpose cutting machines

Specialist devices of all types are available. There are two which are likely to be seen in general use. They are:

* sample-cutting machines – which are usually miniature rotary cutters, used for cutting samples or very small (less than 1.5 cm or half an inch) lays

* cutting-off machines – a miniature rotary cutter, as a sample-cutting machine, which attaches to a handle-and-track system so that it cuts cleanly and swiftly across the fabric as each ply is being spread.

Both these pieces of equipment are beginning to replace scissor-cutting. The increased occurrence of RSI (repetitive strain injury) makes the installation of this type of machinery a significant consideration for those seeking to improve occupation health and safety.

Accessories

Manufacturers of cutting machines also supply a wide range of accessories. The cutting room, like any place where a mechanical process is carried out, may be expected to contain a stock of accessories for occasional use.

The cutting-room accessories store-cupboard might be expected to contain: sharpening belts, sharpening blocks, electric cord extensions and support springs, lamps, spare blades, shears, scissors, pins, drills, lubricants, silicone sprays, adhesives, weights, trolleys.

Some items, such as cord extensions, have an obvious use. Other equipment has a use which is peculiar to the cutting room. Here is a conducted tour, with commentary, through the accessories store-cupboard.

CLAMPS are used in the constant battle between the cutter, who wants fabric to stay precisely where it has been put, and the fabric plies which tend to move when touched. The clamps hold the plies together to eliminate or at least reduce the movement of fabric in the lay.

WEIGHTS are mainly used to stop movement in the lay. Because they are instantly removable, they can be utilised when the actual process of cutting is taking place. Because they are extremely handy, weights tend to be used for manual laying-up and for any task which requires fabric, paper or patterns to be held still.

ADHESIVE, PINS AND STAPLES are all used to fasten the marker to the top of the lay when during the cutting process. The pins and/or staples may be placed in the waste (not waist) sections of the marker. But care is necessary. Pins and staples should be kept well out of the paths taken by the blade of the cutting machine.

Adhesive, usually from a spray can, is extensively used in the cutting-room for glueing the marker to the lay. There is a special way to do this.

Adhesive is sprayed onto the underside of the marker. The paper marker is then positioned onto the lay. Provided the paper (not the fabric) is sprayed, there will be no adhesive residue deposited on the fabric. In addition, a good adhesive will allow the marker, once positioned, to be lifted and repositioned to improve its location.

DRILLS are used, as might be expected, for making holes. A drillhole in a garment component is an aid to its quick and accurate assembly. There is a wide selection of drills. Each has a particular task and is suitable for a particular fabric type. Consult your supplier or chief cutter.

Whichever drill is selected, one simple rule applies. The aim is to make a hole in exactly the same place in each of the fabric plies. This can only be done if the drill is held and used at a precise right-angle (90 degrees) to the cutting table.

There are other general rules concerning the use of drills. For example: the finer the fabric, the finer the drill. And another: beware of a hot drill and a fabric with a significant content of synthetic fibres – fusion might take place.

When using loose-woven fabrics, a chalk or fluorescent drill might be needed. This is a drill which, in use, passes through a reservoir of chalk and/or paste which contains a fluorescent dye. The action of the drill takes the marking substance through the lay, depositing a little around each hole. In this way a hole, even if it has partially closed, is easily found by the machinist.

Among readily-available drills, there are: spiral, dye, thread, hot, chalk, fluorescent, cold and hollow drills. All have their task and place in the cutting operation.

SILICONE LUBRICANTS are usually marketed in spray cans. They are primarily used to coat pieces of machinery (both cutting and sewing) with a silicone deposit. This allows the fabric ease of movement around or over the machine. For example, when silicone is sprayed onto the baseplate of a cutting machine, a drag is reduced to a glide.

RULERS AND SET-SQUARES are used in marking as in any other industrial drawing process: to make straight lines and right-angles. Most cutting-rooms tend to use metal rulers, which are tough, rather than wood or plastic drawing implements which are susceptible to damage and/or distortion.

CUTTING
CRAFT AND TECHNIQUES

CUTTING IS A blend of craft skills and management techniques which cannot be learned solely from a book. But it is possible to acquire some useful guidelines.

The aim, when cutting, is to develop the ability to work with good speed and to achieve excellent quality. Much of the cutter's ability comes from frequent practice. It is also possible to learn from the experience of others.

For example:

1 It is invariably best to cut from one end of the lay to another.

2 The pieces to cut are the pieces closest to the cutter. Cut the edges which are within easy reach. Pieces which are not within easy reach may have to be cut in blocks, clamped, then moved into a better cutting position.

3 When cutting each piece, cut as many sides as possible without removing it from the lay. The last cut should detach it. While a piece remains attached, it is held firm and is unlikely to move during cutting.

4 Clamps should be used whenever possible. This keeps the already-cut sides of the lay perpendicular (at right-angles) to the table, ensuring the accuracy of cut-piece sizes.

5 If there is a choice, cut small pieces from the lay before big pieces. While they are part of the lay, the small pieces remain stable.

Sample cutting

Most garments, particularly fashion garments, are still sold to retailers from ranges of manufacturers' samples. Buyers like to see made-up examples of seasonal or up-date injection ranges.

While computer technology now allows designs to be illustrated with almost three-dimensional reality in very accurate colours, samples are still made of a selected range for buyers' final appraisal.

A sample range is usually produced by sample machinists, working for the designer or design department. But in many companies the cutting room would take over (or assist with) the cutting of the sample range.

Apart from applying the same rules to sample cutting which apply to production cutting, the sample cutter must carry out a second task.

The amount of fabric used in the garment must be calculated and recorded. This is a vital element of the costing process. The cutter must "take a yardage for a costing".

There are two methods adopted within the industry. One seeks a "sample-size yardage" while the other produces an "all-sizes yardage".

SAMPLE-SIZE YARDAGE is calculated by measuring and recording the amount of fabric used in the construction of a sample-sized (usually size 10 or 12) garment.

AVERAGE-SIZE YARDAGE is a measurement and record of the fabric used in cutting the smallest size, then in cutting the largest size, then in calculating an average. (The simple mathematics is to add the smallest yardage to the largest yardage, then to divide the result by two.)

The first set of samples (usually single samples) to be made up are invariably examined by the designers and the marketing experts, usually for the first time. There are often alterations and variations of style.

A second set of samples, sometimes called the repeat samples, is then produced (usually one for each of the agents, wholesalers or salespersons). These are the modified versions. The garments to be produced in bulk will be like the repeats. Theirs is the significant yardage.

Cutting variations

Not every garment is cut in the same way. Though the majority of apparel manufacturers in Australia tend to use cutting machines as described, some are beginning to use computer-controlled cutters (which can cut using a variety of methods, from laser beams to water jets) while others adopt different techniques which suit a particular set of circumstances.

The **BAND KNIFE**, which resembles the woodworkers band-saw, is a belt-shaped cutting blade which rotates and operates vertically. It is static. It stands in one place, its cutting edge facing the operator, who pushes plies of fabric against it.

For this process the lay must be split into segments, and each segment brought to the knife. The marker-maker must bear this in mind and plan the marker accordingly.

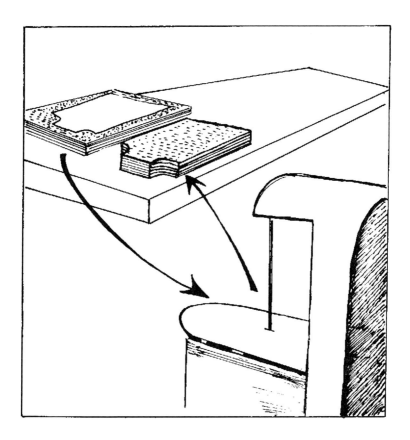

The **DIE-CUTTING** process is very accurate and can deal with shapes which (perhaps because they contain awkward notches or pinking) would be difficult to cut in the more usual way.

The dies are actually knives of hardened steel which have been formed into the shape of the piece they are to cut. These knives are then pressed down, using a special "clicking" machine process, onto the fabric. (Picture a scone-cutter, descending regularly and mechanically onto a flat sheet of dough.)

Die-cutting is very accurate. Each cut is identical to every other. It is a speedy process, once the die has been made and set up and the cutting can be carried out by relatively unskilled labour.

But a die is an expensive item and to pay its way it requires a long commercial life. For this reason it is seldom seen in any section of the fashion industry where the shape of the garment is likely to change each season.

It is more likely to be used in the manufacture of men's shirts and women's underwear. There, particularly in the production of small and accurate items like shirt collars and cuffs to be handled by specialist machines, the die-cutter is in its element.

"THE BIG PICTURE" KEEPS CHANGING

CUTTING is one of a series of processes. When the series is working well, it creates a garment of good design, and from fabric of the right type, price and quality, makes it into an attractive sample which generates lots of orders.

The cutting room interprets these orders (quantity, size, colour, style and delivery date) and produces all the cut components which can be assembled into garments, then invoiced and delivered to wholesalers and retailers.

The entire sequence of events must happen, as planned by the company's managers, so that time and cost projections are met. When everything operates according to schedule, the company makes a profit and stays in business.

If one element goes seriously wrong, the delicate balance — and the prospect of profit — is lost. Each process in the series must be right, first time, every time.

☐　　☐　　☐　　☐

The relationship between each of the processes in the series is crucial.

There is the simple work-to-work relationship. For example, the cutting room must pass on the right number of components, of the right size and colour at the right time or the production department will not be able to assemble them into garments to fulfill orders — and hard-won sales will be lost.

Then there is the far more complicated communications relationship. For example, however good the designer, he/she needs feedback from the sales department on what the retailers want to stock and expect to sell, and from the fabric makers on how the market is reacting to colour and pattern innovations.

The cutting room can play an essential part in this communication process, too. A good cutter can often make a design suggestion about the most cost-effective way to achieve a particular effect. Similarly, a production expert could suggest a cutting refinement while a cutter may suggest an improved method of assembly.

Many of the elements of the garment industry are variables. Few are constants.

There is a "big picture" in the industry. But it is constantly changing. Up-to-date information is important. Often it is vital. The cutter who keeps his/her head down over the table and takes no interest in the other processes in the sequence may one day look up to find that everyone else has gone home because the company has closed.

There are a hundred ways in which those in the cutting room can make their contribution. Essentially, they can provide their best effort and offer their best understanding. Here is a checklist of the key areas.

PAPERWORK can be an annoying interruption. But a company which does not know what is in stock, or which does not convert fabric (a cost) into saleable garments (a profit maker) with every possible speed is likely to lose money.

So stock received must be checked accurately and swiftly for quantity and quality. And incoming deliveries of fabric and accessories must be scheduled to ensure that things arrive exactly as and when required. Anything arriving too early is tying up money and burning away profit. Anything arriving too late is either adding cost to production through haste and overtime, or annoying customers through late deliveries or unreliable quality, or both.

UNDERSTANDING the problems of the other segments of the company (and realising that if anyone falls down on the job, everyone suffers) is a cutting room essential

For example, the production division can do its job effectively only if it receives accurately-cut components exactly on time. It is up to the cutting room staff to ensure that everything, from the acceptance of fabric deliveries to the maintenance of cutting machinery, happens when it should.

Garment manufacturers often sub-contract to outworker groups or companies. Such outworkers frequently have a particular expertise and specialise in handling fine fabrics, or denim, or knits, or embroidery, or screen printing. Outworkers have exactly the same problems to deal with as in-house production departments. So a smooth and regular workflow to sub-contractors has to produce better output and an easier working relationship than a series of last-minute changes and panic attacks.

Finally, the cutting room must understand itself. Every cutting room has limitations. The length and width of available cutting-table space, the availability of fabric storage space, the speed and efficiency of available machinery and the skill levels of available staff will all impose limits on output. Good cutting room planning will be neither pessimistic nor optimistic. It will be realistic.

BUYING — a number of suppliers provide a garment manufacturer with essential raw materials. The materials fall into two main categories: fabric and trim (or accessories). Both are usually selected by the designers.

The cutting room and the production department can make two contributions to the buying process. First, each can offer an expert appraisal of fabric. Will it cut and sew well ? Are there likely to be problems? Is there a better way to achieve the designer's desired effect ?

Next, each can ensure that the delivery schedules for both fabric and trim will be realistic — neither early nor late — so that components and accessories both arrive at the right place at the right time.

TRANSLATION — the cutting room would normally receive from the design department all the graded patterns it needs to complete the company's cutting orders. Before translating a pattern into a component, the prudent cutter will check the work of others by casting an eye over both sample and pattern pieces.

The earlier a problem is faced, the better the solution. So worries should be discussed by cutter and designer at sample-making time, and should not wait until there are impending deadlines for bulk manufacture.

Continued growth in the use of computer-operated grading and marker-making systems (which are usually operated by combined design and cutting-room staff) appears to be reducing the problems in this area.

But specialised expertise can lead to misunderstandings. If the cutting room forsees a problem and wishes to mark, spread or cut a style differently from the way in which the pattern is marked, the nature of the change (and the reasons for suggesting it) should be made clear to the designer.

As the designer may point out, there is no advantage in "saving" a few metres of fabric if, in doing so, the cutter reduces the attractiveness and saleability of a garment.

MARKETING — the needs of the market are never far away from any section of a garment manufacturing company. The company exists to serve the market. The market does not exist to serve the company.

The face-to-face relationship between garment manufacturer and retailer is the responsibility of the sales department. But the cutting room has a relationship which is just as close. On the retailer's rails hang the garments which were marked, spread and cut by the cutting room.

If the quality standards have been achieved and if the bulk garments are a faithful copy of the sample, the retailer will accept and promote them.

But retailing is, to a degree, a form of guesswork. Retailers who have predicted wrongly can soon become disenchanted with slow-moving stock. Part of the problem is likely to become the manufacturer's, because a retailer with a slow-moving line of garments and a great deal of competitive pressure may be tempted to seek any detailed "fault" so that the non-selling range may be returned to the manufacturer.

ASSEMBLY — perhaps the closest relationship between any two segments of the garment manufacturing process is the relationship which exists between the cutting room and the assembly section. This remains constant whether assembly is carried out by in-house machinists, outworker groups, or a combination of both.

Imagine an operator who is trying to assemble a garment from pieces which were not cut "on grain", or were not the exact size or shape, or are missing the required notches and drillholes, or are cut from fabric which contains faults.

If the operator manages to assemble the garment, it is likely to take extra time, so will cost far more than estimated and may well be delivered behind schedule. Possibly, even after assembly, the garment will contain faults and be a "second" and saleable only at reduced price. At worst, the garment will be unsaleable.

A detailed analysis of a garment manufacturing operation would show that each garment is the product of the combined craft skills, creative flair, management ability and marketing know-how of the people involved. Without any one segment, the rest would be unable to function effectively.

But a collection of skills, on its own, is not enough. Skilled people are good. Well-informed skilled people are better. Best of all are people who know their craft, who appreciate the skills of others, and who can keep up with the constant changes in the world in which they operate.

Such people, like the garments which they produce, would be a cut above the rest.

FABRIC IN WORK — FINGERS INTACT

Alive and well in the cutting room

THERE IS NO SHORT CUT to safety. Neither is safety the sole responsibility of any individual or group. Safety in a cutting room is a matter of concern for everyone — the people who built it, the people who own it, the people who maintain it and the people who work in it.

Safety is built into the country's legislation. There are Safety Acts, both Federal and State, which are relevant to the garment manufacturing industry. They set legal requirements and establish standards which are aimed at protecting workers from industrial injuries.

But the Government cannot be the only responsible body, even though it creates the laws aimed at controlling the allocation of blame and the payment of compensation. Both the employer and the employee are equally responsible.

The employer must provide safe and healthy working conditions. The employee must do nothing which endangers either him/herself or anyone else.

In every State there is a WorkCover Authority which produces books and pamphlets explaining the dangers and the remedies. It seems sensible for everyone to take the trouble to investigate his/her position.

There is even a responsibility for employers to ensure that employees are fully informed. A cutting room supervisor may have started as a junior, gaining promotion without ever having been given any formal safety training.

Such a person might be totally unaware of the legal and social reponsibility which he/she carries, both personally and on behalf of the employing company. In most areas there are accredited TAFE courses on marking and cutting in which safe work practice is an integral part.

Safety in the cutting-room

A cutting machine is twice as dangerous as most other machines. Not only does it have the usual number of moving parts and projections, which are a hazard, it also has an extremely sharp and uncovered blade at the front end.

It makes good sense to treat a cutting machine with a great deal of respect. There are rules of operation which must be followed when the machine is in use. And there are rules of maintenance which must be carried out between times.

Safety in use

1 The operator should wear a chain-mail "butcher's" glove on the hand which is not holding the machine. This simple but effective safety measure is being adopted all over the world.

2 Anyone who has long hair, or a long beard (or even both) should pin or tie it back so that it is well away from the machine's moving parts. When negotiating a tricky curve, a cutter's head can be very close to a machine which contains a fast-spinning electric motor and a series of drive-wheels.

3 The safest place for the electric cable which supplies power to a cutting machine is attached to a runner system suspended over the centre of the table. If such a system is not available, the cutter should place the cable over one shoulder, leading away from the table-top. If an active blade comes into contact with a live electric cable, the operator could be electrocuted.

4 Sharpen the blade regularly, during cutting sessions as well as between them. A sharp blade gives a clean and accurate cut. A blunt blade can drag, causing problems of accuracy and danger.

5 Cutting machines are fitted with guards. Use them. Whenever the machine is running, the front "blade" guard should be down. While actually cutting, the guard should be set so that it is just above the fabric plies.

6 A single, smooth sheet of paper should always be placed between the fabric plies and the cutting table surface. The paper helps to create a smooth run and clean cut. This is always true, whether the cutter is working on a few samples or a bulk run.

7 Weights and clamps are an enormous help to a cutter. Many experienced cutters refer to weights and clamps as their "extra pair of hands". With weights and clamps the lay is held still during the cutting process and the resultant pattern pieces are more likely to be identical and accurate.

☐　　☐　　☐　　☐

Safety in maintenance

Regular and routine attention are important if a cutting machine is to have a reasonably long and useful life. A single golden rule applies to cutting machines, as to all electrical appliances.

Before any adjustment, repair or maintenance work is carried out, turn the machine off and disconnect it from its power supply. After that:

1 A cutting machine should be regularly oiled. A machine which runs every second or third day should be oiled at least once a week. Follow the manufacturer's recommendations.

2 Lint and fluff will build up on a cutting machine very quickly. This must be cleaned off frequently. An ideal tool for the job is a small paintbrush.

3 The blade and the sharpening belt (or block) should be changed regularly. A blade is ready to be changed when about 50% of its sharpened edge has been worn away. When changing the blade of a straight-blade machine, it it sensible to change the sharpening belt at the same time.

When a new blade has been fitted, start and "test run" it (with the machine turned away from the operator) for a few seconds, then sharpen the blade eight or more times before continuing to use it.

4 All electrical attachments, fittings and cords must be regularly inspected and kept in good repair. Electrical work carried out by a qualified electrician is usually reliable. Electrical work carried out by an unqualified person is usually unreliable.

5 The underside of a cutting-machine's baseplate is usually fitted with wheels which allow it to move across the cutting table. They can become clogged with lint and fluff and should be kept clean, but not oiled. (Oil may be good for wheels, but it is bad for fabrics.) Clogged wheels may be freed by running them back and forth over the shiny side of a sheet of brown paper which has been spread out on the cutting table.

Commonsense

Whatever the formal tuition and the legal obligation, the final approach to safety must be left to the good sense of each individual. Here are some commonsense guidelines.

Commonsense safety guidelines

1 Good, adequate lighting which for preference should be a blend of natural and electric light.

2 A cutting room table should be of a height which is appropriate to both the work and the worker. A stable purpose-built step (not an upturned crate) should be provided to enable a cutter to reach across a table.

3 All surfaces and floors, on around and under the cutting table, should be kept absolutely clear. A non-slip floor covering is also a necessity.

4 Passing "people traffic" should be kept away from cutting tables, perhaps by marking walkways on the floors.

5 Excellent ventilation of the cutting room is essential. Fabric not only produces a great deal of dust and lint, it is often dressed with insecticides, and when its plastic wrapping is removed, it releases toxic fumes.

6 There are three types of fire extinguisher: one for oil-based, one for cellulose-based and one for electrical fires. A cutting room needs all three — regularly maintained and clearly labelled.

7 Every cutting room should be equipped with an up-to-date first-aid kit and an oxy-vivor. There should also be at least one employee who has been trained in first aid.

8 An overhead and correctly tracked electric power source should be provided for each cutting table. Power cables which trail across the floor or the table are dangerous.

9 Every piece of machinery and electric cable should be inspected and maintained, by a qualified expert, on a regular scheduled basis.

10 Blunt and ragged cutting blades cause accidents. Sharpening blocks and emery bands should be used regularly and, as they wear out in the process, replaced regularly.

11 Before cutting a lay, ensure that the fabric plies have paper under them. This aids both safety and accuracy.

12 Never leave a cutting machine unattended. A machine should not be left running without a cutter's hand on its controls.

13 Cutting machines require the removal of fluff and lint from castors and baseplate at least once every day.

14 The guards fitted to cutting machines are there to protect the operator. The rear guard (covering the balance wheel) should always be kept closed. When the machine is running, the foot guard (around the blade) should be fully down. When the machine is in use, the guard should be set at a height which minimises fabric movement and maximises operator protection.

15 Do not smoke, in any part of the cutting room, ever.

Self protection

There are many simple things which the staff in a cutting room can do (and should do) to protect themselves.

1 Loose hair and long beards should be tied back to reduce the chance of their catching in a machine's moving parts.

2 Dangling jewellery and accessories, including unbuttoned sleeves, should be avoided. Wear close-fitting clothes.

3 Footwear should be of medium to heavy weight, made with a fully covering upper.

A final word about gloves.

It requires very little pressure for a cutting machine's blade to slice its way through skin, muscle and bone.

TAFE students who are being trained for the cutting room today are being taught to use a glove. It is metal mesh — in fact it is a butcher's chain-mail glove. It is worn on the hand which does not hold and operate the cutting machine. It really does protect a hand which inadvertly has been left lying in the path of the blade.

Someone wearing a glove might suffer a small cut in an accident which, without the glove, would have severed a finger.

Experienced cutters, who have spent many years working with a bare hand, may find it difficult to adjust to wearing a glove. Following an accident, they may find it even harder to adjust to working without a finger or a hand.

For anyone (perhaps a self-employed person) using a cutting machine while on his/her own, a chain-mail glove is essential. It could reduce an injury, allowing someone in distress to reach a telephone and help.

It is no coincidence that cutters who are "old hands" are likely to have one or more flat-topped fingers.

INDEX

INDEX

INDEX